Supporting Phonics and Spelling

FOR AGES 5–6

Andrew Brodie

Contents

This page can also be used for planning and monitoring purposes. Photocopy the sheet to create an individual record sheet for each child. As you work through the programme of activities, draw a horizontal line through each phoneme and each word if you feel the child is confident with it. If you feel that the child needs further practice, draw a ring round the phoneme or word. Once the child reaches the later sets, you should find that there are more lines than rings as revision and consolidation are key features of this series.

Introduction

Supporting Phonics and Spelling is aimed at children in mainstream classrooms who have been identified as needing 'additional' or 'different' literacy support, particularly in phonics and spelling. The activities can be used by anyone working with children who fall into this category, whether you are a teacher, classroom assistant or parent.

Typically the five to six year-old children for whom the book is intended will be working at the levels expected of Foundation stage or may simply need extra help in tackling the level of work appropriate for Year 1. Their difficulties may be short-term, and could be overcome with extra practice and support on a one-to-one or small group basis, or they may be long-term, where such support enables them to make progress but at a level behind their peer group. The activities in this book provide exactly what these children need – systematic repetition and practice of early phonic skills, based on a strong foundation of synthetic phonics and the best features of analytic phonics. The *Supporting Phonics and Spelling* series reflects the best practice in teaching spelling through phonics. It provides an approach that is:

- Systematic
- Multi-sensory
- Based on speaking and listening
- Linked closely to reading skills

This book is organised into three-page sets. It is vital that the teaching assistant or class teacher reads the 'Teacher's notes' on 'Sheet a' before starting the lesson. The first page in each set introduces specific phonemes and provides a good opportunity for the teacher and child to sound them out together. Children can also use their multi-sensory skills at this stage by drawing the letters in sand or making them out of dough or modelling clay. The second worksheet revises the same phonemes, but with a particular emphasis on speaking, listening and writing. The final worksheet in the set features a list of words containing the phonemes for further practice and consolidation. When used together, the three worksheets provide a thorough grounding in the phonic knowledge and skills that children need for confident reading, writing and spelling.

All the worksheets can be used on their own or alongside other literacy schemes that are already established within your school. The activities are simple and self-explanatory and the instruction text is deliberately kept to a minimum to make the pages easy to use for adults and less daunting for children to follow.

We recommend that the children use the *Supporting Phonics and Spelling* worksheets on a daily basis for approximately 20 minutes. Regular practice of previous learning is an integral part of the series. In completing the activities, teachers should place particular emphasis on speaking and listening skills.

Children generally achieve the greatest success in an atmosphere of support and encouragement. Praise from a caring adult can be the best reward for the children's efforts. The worksheets and activities in this book will provide many opportunities for children to enjoy these successes. The development of a positive attitude and the resulting increase in self-esteem will help them with all of their schoolwork.

Definitions and explanations of terms

(Please note that some publications will give slightly different definitions.)

Phoneme
A phoneme is a unit of sound and can be represented by:
one letter e.g. /b/ as in **b**at   two letters e.g. /ee/ as in sw**ee**t
three letters e.g. /ear/ as in n**ear**
Note that a phoneme can be represented in several different ways
e.g. the sound /ee/ can be represented by:
    ee as in f**ee**t   **ei** as in c**ei**ling   **ie** as in ch**ie**f
    ea as in n**ea**t   **i** as in sk**i**   **e_e** as in P**e**t**e**

Vowel phoneme
A vowel phoneme makes an open sound and always contains at least one vowel – you usually have to open your mouth to say it.
Examples of vowel phonemes are:
    /a/ as in b**a**t   /ie/ as in cr**ie**s   /oo/ as in b**oo**k
    /ur/ as in t**ur**n   /ow/ as in t**ow**n

Consonant phoneme
A consonant phoneme always contains at least one consonant and usually involves closing the mouth, 'biting' the lower lip, or touching the roof of the mouth with the tongue. (There are exceptions e.g. /h/). Examples of consonant phonemes are:
    /b/ as in **b**at   /f/ as in **ph**otograph
    /th/ as in **th**ey   /ng/ as in si**ng**

Grapheme
A grapheme is a letter, a pair of letters or a group of letters representing a single sound e.g. **ee**, **ei**, **ie**, **ea**, **i** and **e_e** are all graphemes representing the sound /ee/.

Grapheme/phoneme correspondence
The relationship between letters and the sounds that they represent.

Digraph
A digraph consists of two letters representing a single sound. So, for example, the grapheme **ch** is a consonant digraph because it is made up of two consonants. The grapheme **ee** is a vowel digraph and although it contains a consonant, **ow** is also a vowel digraph, because it makes an open sound like a vowel does.

Split digraph
A split digraph consists of two vowels separated by a consonant to make one phoneme e.g.   **e_e** as in P**e**t**e**   **i_e** as in m**i**n**e**   **a_e** as in c**a**m**e**

Trigraph
A trigraph is a group of three letters representing a single sound. The vowel phonemes /air/ and /ear/ are trigraphs.

Cluster
A cluster consists of two or more letters making more than one sound. For example:
t   **h**   **r**   are three letters that can make the cluster **thr**, which consists of the phonemes /th/ and /r/.

Blending
Blending is the process of combining different sounds (phonemes) to be able to say a particular word or to make up part of a word e.g.
/sh/   /i/   /p/   can be blended to make the word ship.

/th/   /r/   are blended to make the cluster **thr**. Sometimes a cluster like this will be called a blend.

Segmenting
Segmenting is the process of splitting a word into its different phonemes to be able to spell it e.g. **ship** can be segmented into the three phonemes /sh/ /i/ /p/.

Onset and rime
The terms 'onset' and 'rime' are used together when analysing words. For example, in the word 'cat' the phoneme represented by the letter 'c' is described as the onset and the final cluster 'at' is described as the rime. Note that words that end with a particular rime always rhyme but words that rhyme do not always contain the same rime! For example, cat, rat and bat all end with the rime 'at' and all rhyme. But the words tough and muff rhyme but have the rimes 'ough' and 'uff'.

vc
vowel/consonant e.g. the word *it*

cv
consonant/vowel e.g. the word *be*

cvc
consonant/vowel/consonant e.g. the word *cat*

ccvc
consonant/consonant/vowel/consonant e.g. the word *shop*

cvcc
consonant/vowel/consonant/consonant e.g. the word *fast*

Andrew Brodie: Supporting Phonics & Spelling © A & C Black Publishers Ltd. 2006

An introduction to phonemes

Language can be analysed by considering the separate sounds that combine to make up spoken words. These sounds are called phonemes and the English language has more than forty of them. It is possible to concentrate on forty-two main phonemes but here we list forty-four phonemes including those that are commonly used only in some regions of the country.

It is helpful to look at each phoneme individually and then at some sample words that demonstrate how the phoneme is represented by different graphemes as shown in the list below. Try reading each word out loud to spot the phoneme in each one. For the simple vowel sounds the graphemes are shown in bold text.

Vowel phonemes	Sample words
/a/	b**a**t
/e/	l**e**g, g**ue**ss, h**ea**d, s**ai**d, s**ay**s
/i/	b**i**g, plant**e**d, b**u**sy, cr**y**stal, d**e**cide, **e**xact, g**ui**lt, r**e**peat
/o/	d**o**g, **ho**nest, w**a**s, qu**a**rrel, tr**ou**gh, v**au**lt, y**ach**t (the ch is silent)
/u/	b**u**g, l**o**ve, bl**oo**d, c**o**mfort, r**ou**gh, y**ou**ng
/ae/	rain, day, game, navy, weigh, they, great, rein
/ee/	been, team, field, these, he, key, litre, quay, suite
/ie/	pie, high, sign, my, bite, child, guide, guy, haiku
/oe/	boat, goes, crow, cone, gold, sew
/ue/	soon, do, July, blue, chew, June, bruise, shoe, you, move, through
/oo/	book, put
/ar/	barn, bath (regional), laugh (regional), baa, half, clerk, heart, guard
/ur/	Thursday, girl, her, learn, word
/or/	born, door, warm, all, draw, cause, talk, aboard, abroad, before, four, bought, taught
/ow/	brown, found, plough
/oi/	join, toy, buoy
/air/	chair, pear, care, where, their, prayer
/ear/	near, cheer, here, weird, pier

Try saying this vowel phoneme in the sample words:

/er/	fast**er**, g**a**zump, curr**a**nt, wooll**e**n, circ**us**
	Not to be confused with the phoneme /ur/, this phoneme is very similar to /u/ but is slightly different in some regions.

Consonant phonemes with sample words

/b/	bag, rub
/d/	dad, could
/f/	off, calf, fast, graph, tough
/g/	ghost, girl, bag
/h/	here, who
/j/	bridge, giraffe, huge, jet
/k/	kite, antique, cat, look, quiet, choir, sock, six (note that the sound made by the letter x is a blend of the phonemes /k/ and /s/)
/l/	leg, crawl, full
/m/	mug, climb, autumn
/n/	now, gnash, knight, sign, fun
/p/	peg, tap
/r/	run, wrote
/s/	cinema, goose, listen, psalm, scene, see, sword, yes, less
/t/	ten, sit, receipt
/v/	vest, love
/w/	wet
/wh/	when (regional)
/y/	yes
/z/	choose, was, zoo
/th/	the, with
/th/	thank, path
/ch/	cheer, such, match
/sh/	shop, rush, session, chute
/zh/	usual
/ng/	thing, think

For some phonemes you may dispute some of the examples that we have listed. This may be due to regional variations in pronunciation. Disputing the sounds is a positive step as it ensures that you are analysing them!

It is not necessary to teach the children all the graphemes for each phoneme but to be ready and aware when pupils suggest words to you to represent a particular sound. They are not wrong with their suggestions and should be praised for recognising the phoneme. You can then show them how the words that they have suggested are written but that normally the particular sound is represented by a specific grapheme.

Andrew Brodie: Supporting Phonics & Spelling © A & C Black Publishers Ltd. 2006

	Words	Phoneme
Words that open with a simple vowel sound, ie vc and vcc words:	**a**m **a**t **a**nd	/a/
		/e/
	in **i**s **i**t	/i/
	of **o**n	/o/
	up	/u/

cvc words that appear in the Reception word list:

Words	Phoneme
c**a**n c**a**t d**a**d	/a/
g**e**t y**e**s	/e/
b**i**g	/i/
d**o**g w**a**s	/o/
*(note that the middle letter is **a** but the phoneme is /o/)*	
m**u**m	/u/

cv, ccv and cvv words that appear in the Reception word list:

Words	Phoneme
h**e** m**e** sh**e** th**e** w**e** s**ee**	/ee/
g**o** n**o**	/oe/
t**o** y**ou**	/ue/
m**y**	/ie/
*(here the letter **y** is acting as a vowel so we would consider this word to be a cv word.)*	

Other words from the list

a	come	I	said
all	day	like	they
are	for	look	this
away	going	play	went

Learning objective

Phonemes	**Target words**
Consonants: /b/, /d/, /f/, /g/, /p/, /r/, /w/ Vowel: /i/	big, pig, wig, fig, dig, rig

1a

Teacher's notes

Sheet 1a

- Photocopy this page and cut out the letter tiles.

- Revise the sounds with the child. Depending on your school's policy, you may decide to use the letter names as well as the sounds saying, for example, 'This is letter **b** and it says /b/.' Pronounce the phoneme as it would sound when used in a word, without any additional sounds, e.g. the sound that **b** makes at the start of the word *big* is quite short and subtle.

- When you feel the child is confident with some or all of the phonemes, arrange the letter tiles to make the words *big, pig, wig, fig, dig and rig*. Help the child blend the phonemes to say the words.

Sheet 1b

- When you feel the child is ready, look at Sheet 1b together. Ask him/her to point to the letters at the top of the page and to tell you the sounds they make.

- Dictate the words **big**, **pig**, **wig**, **fig**, **dig**, **rig** one at a time, helping the child segment each word into its phonemes so that s/he can choose the correct letters to match the words. Each word can then be stuck in position on the worksheet and the child can copy the words on to the writing lines underneath.

- As an additional activity you could make up some oral sentences together using some of the words and pointing at these words as you say them, e.g. *The pig has a big wig.* Write down one of the sentences for the child to copy. Encourage him/her to write clearly, following the school's handwriting policy for letter formation, and to start the sentence with a capital letter and to end it with a full stop.

Sheet 1c

- This sheet includes six words with the medial vowel **i** and the final consonant **g**. It could be photocopied for display purposes but could also be used to provide extra practice in writing the words.

- There are three writing lines for each word, one for writing the word quite large and the other two for smaller writing practice. You could write each word on the first of the two smaller writing lines so that the child can copy your writing in the correct style used by your school.

LETTER TILES

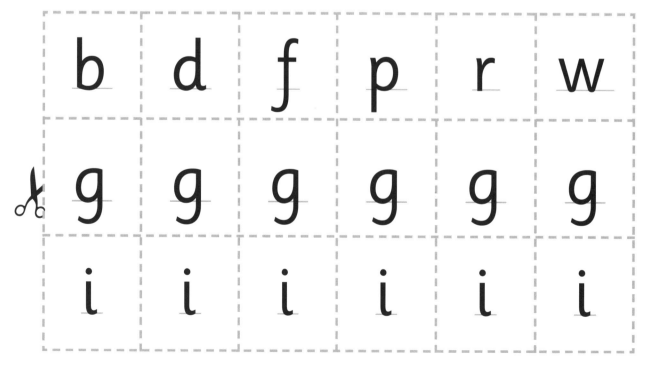

Name: **Date:**

What sounds do the letters make?

b w f p d g r i

Listen to your teacher.
Stick on letters to make the words.

1c

Words for today

big

pig

wig

fig

dig

rig

Andrew Brodie: Supporting Phonics & Spelling © A & C Black Publishers Ltd. 2006

2a

Learning objective

Phonemes
Consonants: /k/, /f/, /m/, /p/, /r/, /v/, /n/
Vowel: /a/

Target words
can, fan, man, pan, ran, van

Teacher's notes

Sheet 2a

- Photocopy this page and cut out the letter tiles.

- Revise the sounds with the child. Depending on your school's policy, you may decide to use the letter names as well as the sounds, saying, for example, 'This is letter **f** and it says /f/.' Pronounce the phoneme as it would sound when used in a word, without any additional sounds, e.g. the sound that **f** makes at the start of the word *fan* is quite short and subtle.

- When you feel the child is confident with some or all of the phonemes, arrange the letter tiles to make the words *can, fan, man, pan, ran, van*. Help the child blend the phonemes to say the words.

Sheet 2b

- When you feel the child is ready, look at Sheet 2b together. Ask him/her to point to the letters at the top of the page and to tell you the sounds they make.

- Dictate the words **can, fan, man, pan, ran, van** one at a time, helping the child segment each word into its phonemes so that s/he can choose the correct letters to match the words.

- As an additional activity you could make up some oral sentences together using some of the words and pointing to these words as you say them, e.g. *The man was in his van. Can I have a dust pan?* Write down one of the sentences for the child to copy. Encourage him/her to write clearly, following the school's handwriting policy, and to start the sentence with a capital letter and to finish with a full stop.

Sheet 2c

- This sheet includes six words with the medial vowel **a** and the final consonant **n**. It could be photocopied for display purposes but could also be used to provide extra practice in writing the words.

- There are three writing lines for each word, one for writing the word quite large and the other two for smaller writing practice. You could write each word on the first of the two smaller writing lines so that the child can copy your writing in the correct style used by your school.

LETTER TILES

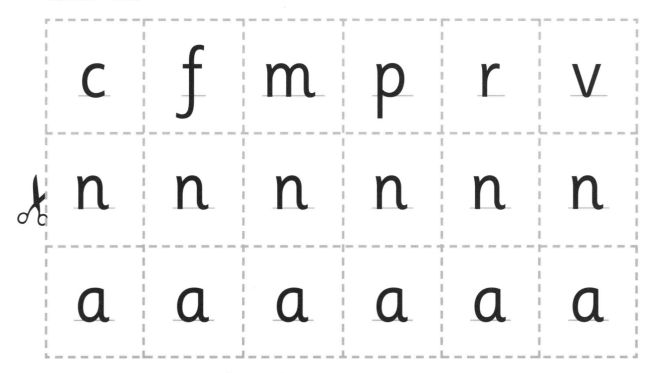

Name: **Date:**

What sounds do the letters make?

c f m p r v n a

Listen to your teacher. Write the words.

Make up your own sentence using some of the words.

Andrew Brodie: Supporting Phonics & Spelling © A & C Black Publishers Ltd. 2006

2c

Name: _____ **Date:** _____

Words for today

can _____ _____

fan _____ _____

man _____ _____

pan _____ _____

ran _____ _____

van _____ _____

3a

Learning objective	
Phonemes **Consonants:** /k/, /g/, /h/, /j/, /n/, /p/, /t/ **Vowel:** /o/	**Target words** got, hot, not, pot, jot, cot

Teacher's notes

Sheet 3a

- Photocopy this page and cut out the letter tiles.

- Revise the sounds with the child. Depending on your school's policy, you may decide to use the letter names as well as the sounds, saying, for example, 'This is letter **c** and it says /k/.' Pronounce the phoneme as it would sound when used in a word, without any additional sounds, e.g. the sound that **c** makes at the start of the word *cot* is quite short and subtle.

- When you feel the child is confident with some or all of the phonemes, arrange the letter tiles to make the words *got, hot, not, pot, jot, cot.* Help the child blend the phonemes to say the words.

Sheet 3b

- When you feel the child is ready, look at Sheet 3b together. Ask him/her to point to the letters at the top of the page and to tell you the sounds they make.

- Read the sentences with the missing words with the child and help him/her write the words in the correct places.

- Show the child the remaining three words. Now cover these words one at a time. Say the word that is covered and help the child to segment the word into its phonemes (sounds) so s/he can write it.

Sheet 3c

- This sheet includes six words with the medial vowel **o** and the final consonant **t**. It could be photocopied for display purposes but could also be used to provide extra practice in writing the words.

- There are three writing lines for each word, one for writing the word quite large and the other two for smaller writing practice. You could write each word on the first of the two smaller writing lines so that the child can copy your writing in the correct style used by your school.

LETTER TILES

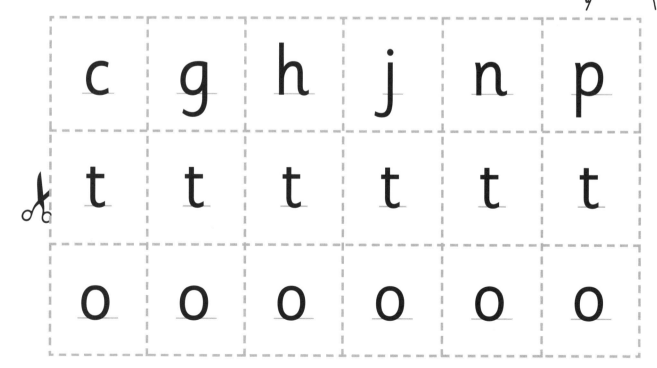

Name: _____   **Date:** _____

What sounds do the letters make?

c g h j n p t o

WORD BANK

got   hot   not   pot   jot   cot

Find the missing words.

Tim got very _____
in the sunshine.

Dad put the baby
in the _____ .

We had to _____
some numbers down.

Now write the other words.

_____   _____   _____

Name: **Date:**

Words for today

got

hot

not

pot

jot

cot

Andrew Brodie: Supporting Phonics & Spelling © A & C Black Publishers Ltd. 2006

4a

Learning objective	
Phonemes **Consonants:** /g/, /m/, /n/, /p/, /t/, /v/, /y/ **Vowel:** /e/	**Target words** get, met, net, pet, vet, yet

Teacher's notes

Sheet 4a

- Photocopy this page and cut out the letter tiles.

- Revise the sounds with the child. Depending on your school's policy, you may decide to use the letter names as well as the sounds, saying, for example, 'This is letter **m** and it says /m/.' Pronounce the phoneme as it would sound when used in a word, without any additional sounds, e.g. the sound that **m** makes at the start of the word *met* is quite short and subtle.

- When you feel the child is confident with some or all of the phonemes, arrange the letter tiles to make the words *get, met, net, pet, vet, yet.* Help the child blend the phonemes to say the words.

Sheet 4b

- When you feel the child is ready, look at Sheet 4b together. Ask him/her to point to the letters at the top of the page and to tell you the sounds they make.

- Dictate the words **get, met, net, pet, vet, yet** one at a time, helping the child segment each word into its phonemes so that s/he can choose the correct letters to match the words. Each word can then be stuck in position on the worksheet and the child can copy the words on to the writing lines underneath.

- As an additional activity you could make up some oral sentences together using some of the words and pointing to these words as you say them, e.g. *Try to get the ball in the net. Have you met the vet yet?* Write down one of the sentences for the child to copy. Encourage him/her to write clearly, following the school's handwriting policy, and to start the sentence with a capital letter and to finish with a full stop.

Sheet 4c

- This sheet includes six words with the medial vowel **e** and the final consonant **t**. It could be photocopied for display purposes but could also be used to provide extra practice in writing the words.

- There are three writing lines for each word, one for writing the word quite large and the other two for smaller writing practice. You could write each word on the first of the two smaller writing lines so that the child can copy your writing in the correct style used by your school.

LETTER TILES

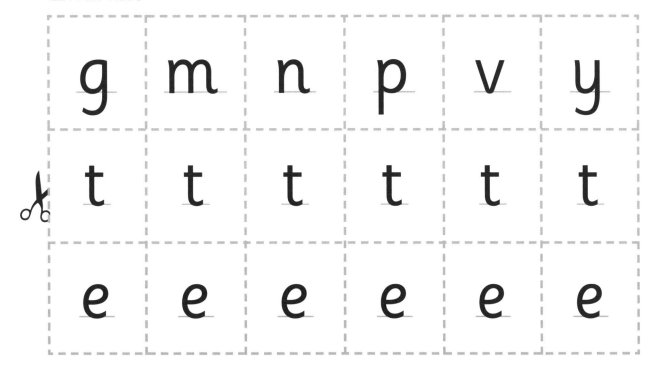

Name: **Date:**

What sounds do the letters make?

g m n p t v y e

Listen to your teacher.
Stick on letters to make the words.

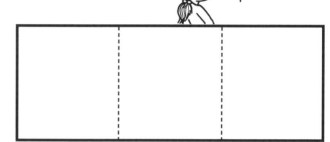

4c

Words for today

get

met

net

pet

vet

yet

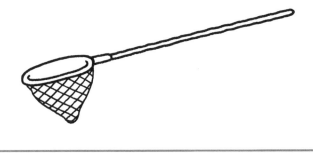

5a

Learning objective	
Phonemes **Consonants:** /b/, /d/, /h/, /s/, /l/, /p/ **Vowel:** /a/	**Target words** bad, dad, had, sad, lad, pad

Teacher's notes

Sheet 5a

- Photocopy this page and cut out the letter tiles.
- Revise the sounds with the child. Depending on your school's policy, you may decide to use the letter names as well as the sounds, saying, for example, 'This is letter **l** and it says /l/.' Pronounce the phoneme as it would sound when used in a word, without any additional sounds.
- When you feel the child is confident with some or all of the phonemes, arrange the letter tiles to make the words *bad, dad, had, sad, lad, pad.* Help the child blend the phonemes to say the words.

Sheet 5b

- When you feel the child is ready, look at Sheet 5b together. Ask him/her to point to the letters at the top of the page and to tell you the sounds they make.
- Dictate the words **bad, dad, had, sad, lad, pad** one at a time, helping the child segment each word into its phonemes so that s/he can choose the correct letters to match the words.
- As an additional activity you could make up some oral sentences together using some of the words and pointing to these words as you say them, e.g. *He is not a bad lad. Dad wrote a note on the pad.* Write down one of the sentences for the child to copy. Encourage him/her to write clearly, following the school's handwriting policy, and to start the sentence with a capital letter and to finish with a full stop.

Sheet 5c

- This sheet includes six words with the medial vowel **a** and the final consonant **d**. It could be photocopied for display purposes but could also be used to provide extra practice in writing the words.
- There are three writing lines for each word, one for writing the word quite large and the other two for smaller writing practice. You could write each word on the first of the two smaller writing lines so that the child can copy your writing in the correct style used by your school.

LETTER TILES

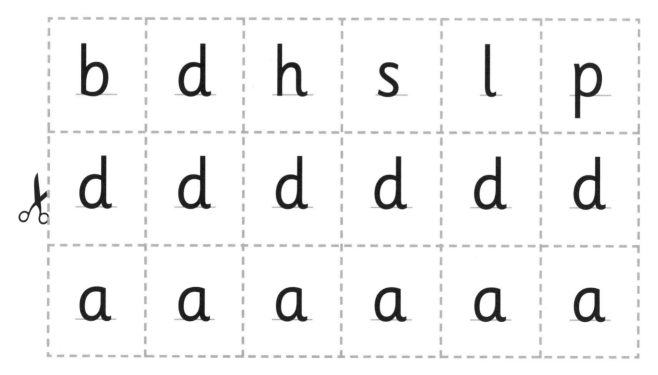

Andrew Brodie: Supporting Phonics & Spelling © A & C Black Publishers Ltd. 2006

Name: _____   **Date:** _____

What sounds do the letters make?

b d h s l p a

Listen to your teacher. Write the words.

_____   _____

_____   _____

_____   _____

Make up your own sentence using some of the words.

_____

_____

Andrew Brodie: Supporting Phonics & Spelling © A & C Black Publishers Ltd. 2006

5c **Name:**   **Date:**

Words for today

bad

dad

had

sad

lad

pad

Andrew Brodie: Supporting Phonics & Spelling © A & C Black Publishers Ltd. 2006

6a

Phonemes
Consonants: /k/, /d/, /f/, /g/, /h/, /j/, /l/
Vowel: /o/

Target words
cog, dog, fog, hog, jog, log

Teacher's notes

Sheet 6a

- Photocopy this page and cut out the letter tiles.

- Revise the sounds with the child. Depending on your school's policy, you may decide to use the letter names as well as the sounds, saying, for example, 'This is letter **g** and it says /g/.' Pronounce the phoneme as it would sound when used at the end of a word, without any additional sounds.

- When you feel the child is confident with some or all of the phonemes, arrange the letter tiles to make the words *cog, dog, fog, hog, jog, log*. Help the child blend the phonemes to say the words.

Sheet 6b

- When you feel the child is ready, look at Sheet 6b together. Ask him/her to point to the letters at the top of the page and to tell you the sounds they make.

- Read the sentences with the missing words with the child and help him/her to write the words in the correct places.

Sheet 6c

- This sheet includes six words with the medial vowel **o** and the final consonant **g**. It could be photocopied for display purposes but could also be used to provide extra practice in writing the words.

- There are three writing lines for each word, one for writing the word quite large and the other two for smaller writing practice. You could write each word on the first of the two smaller writing lines so that the child can copy your writing in the correct style used by your school.

LETTER TILES

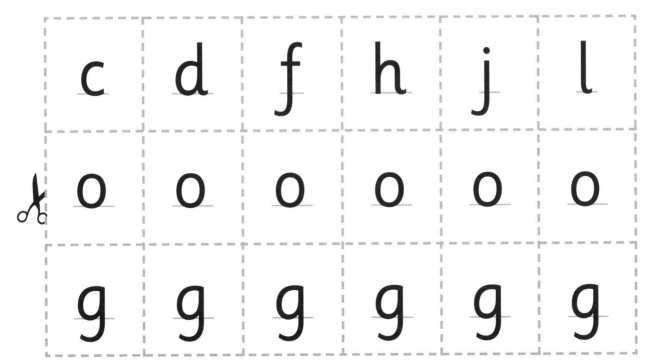

c   d   f   h   j   l

o   o   o   o   o   o

g   g   g   g   g   g

Name: **Date:**

What sounds do the letters make?

c d f g h j l o

WORD BANK

cog   dog   fog   hog   jog   log

Find the missing words.

Sam went out for a

_____ in the park.

Mum got lost
in the _____.

The big _____
jumped over a _____.

Now write the other words.

_____   _____   _____

Andrew Brodie: Supporting Phonics & Spelling © A & C Black Publishers Ltd. 2006

Name: **Date:**

Words for today

cog

dog

fog

hog

jog

log

7a	Learning objective	
	Phonemes Consonants: /b/, /d/, /f/, /n/, /p/, /t/, /w/ Vowel: /i/	**Target words** bin, din, fin, pin, tin, win

Teacher's notes

Sheet 7a

- Photocopy this page and cut out the letter tiles.

- Revise the sounds with the child. Depending on your school's policy, you may decide to use the letter names as well as the sounds, saying, for example, 'This is letter **w** and it says /w/.' Pronounce the phoneme as it would sound when used in a word, without any additional sounds, e.g. the sound that **w** makes at the start of the word *win* is quite short and subtle.

- When you feel the child is confident with some or all of the phonemes, arrange the letter tiles to make the words *bin, din, fin, pin, tin, win*. Help the child blend the phonemes to say the words.

Sheet 7b

- When you feel the child is ready, look at Sheet 7b together. Ask him/her to point to the letters at the top of the page and to tell you the sounds they make.

- Dictate the words **bin, din, fin, pin, tin, win** one at a time, helping the child segment each word into its phonemes so that s/he can choose the correct letters to match the words. Each word can then be stuck in position on the worksheet and the child can copy the words on to the writing lines underneath.

- As an additional activity you could make up some oral sentences together using some of the words and pointing to these words as you say them, e.g. *Put the tin in the bin. I saw the shark's fin*. Write down one of the sentences for the child to copy. Encourage him/her to write clearly, following the school's handwriting policy, and to start the sentence with a capital letter and to finish with a full stop.

Sheet 7c

- This sheet includes six words with the medial vowel **i** and the final consonant **n**. It could be photocopied for display purposes but could also be used to provide extra practice in writing the words.

- There are three writing lines for each word, one for writing the word quite large and the other two for smaller writing practice. You could write each word on the first of the two smaller writing lines so that the child can copy your writing in the correct style used by your school.

LETTER TILES

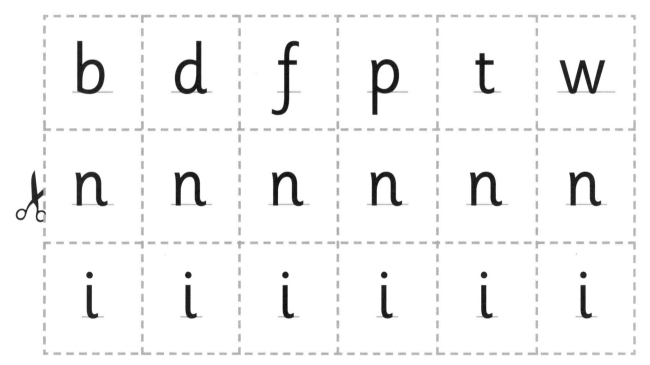

Andrew Brodie: Supporting Phonics & Spelling © A & C Black Publishers Ltd. 2006

What sounds do the letters make?

b d f n p t w i

Listen to your teacher.
Stick on letters to make the words.

7c

Name: _____ **Date:** _____

Words for today

bin _____ _____

din _____ _____

fin _____ _____

pin _____ _____

tin _____ _____

win _____ _____

Learning objective

Phonemes	**Target words**
Consonants: /k/, /g/, /m/, /p/, /t/, /y/, /z/ **Vowel:** /a/	cap, gap, map, tap, yap, zap

Teacher's notes

Sheet 8a

- Photocopy this page and cut out the letter tiles.

- Revise the sounds with the child. Depending on your school's policy, you may decide to use the letter names as well as the sounds, saying, for example, 'This is letter **z** and it says /z/.' Pronounce the phoneme as it would sound when used in a word, without any additional sounds.

- When you feel the child is confident with some or all of the phonemes, arrange the letter tiles to make the words *cap, gap, map, tap, yap, zap*. Help the child blend the phonemes to say the words.

Sheet 8b

- When you feel the child is ready, look at Sheet 8b together. Ask him/her to point to the letters at the top of the page and to tell you the sounds they make.

- Dictate the words **cap, gap, map, tap, yap, zap** one at a time, helping the child segment each word into its phonemes so that s/he can choose the correct letters to match the words.

- As an additional activity you could make up some oral sentences together using some of the words and pointing to these words as you say them, e.g. *The girl wore a baseball cap. Look at the map.* Write down one of the sentences for the child to copy. Encourage him/her to write clearly, following the school's handwriting policy, and to start the sentence with a capital letter and to finish with a full stop.

Sheet 8c

- This sheet includes six words with the medial vowel **i** and the final consonant **g**. It could be photocopied for display purposes but could also be used to provide extra practice in writing the words.

- There are three writing lines for each word, one for writing the word quite large and the other two for smaller writing practice. You could write each word on the first of the two smaller writing lines so that the child can copy your writing in the correct style used by your school.

LETTER TILES

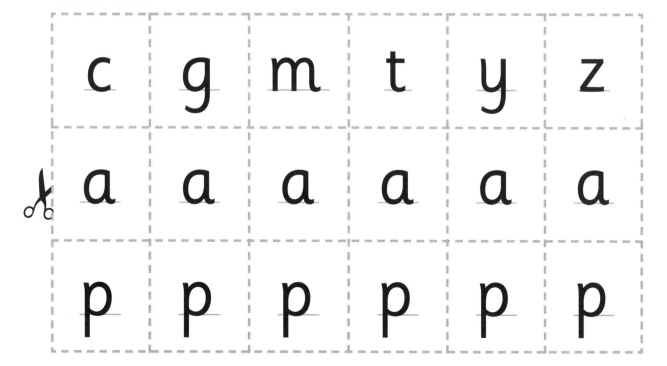

Name: _____ **Date:** _____

What sounds do the letters make?

c g m p t y z a

Listen to your teacher. Write the words.

_____   _____

_____   _____

_____   _____

Make up your own sentence using some of the words.

_____

_____

_____

Andrew Brodie: Supporting Phonics & Spelling © A & C Black Publishers Ltd. 2006

Name: **Date:**

Words for today

cap

gap

map

tap

yap

zap

Andrew Brodie: Supporting Phonics & Spelling © A & C Black Publishers Ltd. 2006

Learning objective

9a	**Phonemes** **Consonants:** /k/, /f/, /m/, /p/, /r/, /s/, /t/ **Vowel:** /a/	**Target words** cat, mat, pat, rat, sat, fat

Teacher's notes

Sheet 9a

- Photocopy this page and cut out the letter tiles.

- Revise the sounds with the child. Depending on your school's policy, you may decide to use the letter names as well as the sounds, saying, for example, 'This is letter **p** and it says /p/.' Pronounce the phoneme as it would sound when used in a word, without any additional sounds.

- When you feel the child is confident with some or all of the phonemes, arrange the letter tiles to make the words *cat, mat, pat, rat, sat, fat.* Help the child blend the phonemes to say the words.

Sheet 9b

- When you feel the child is ready, look at Sheet 9b together. Ask him/her to point to the letters at the top of the page and to tell you the sounds they make.

- Read the sentences with the missing words with the child and help him/her to write the words in the correct places.

Sheet 9c

- This sheet includes six words with the medial vowel **a** and the final consonant **t**. It could be photocopied for display purposes but could also be used to provide extra practice in writing the words.

- There are three writing lines for each word, one for writing the word quite large and the other two for smaller writing practice. You could write each word on the first of the two smaller writing lines so that the child can copy your writing in the correct style used by your school.

LETTER TILES

c	f	m	p	r	s
t	t	t	t	t	t
a	a	a	a	a	a

Andrew Brodie: Supporting Phonics & Spelling © A & C Black Publishers Ltd. 2006

Name: _____   **Date:** _____

What sounds do the letters make?

c f m p r s t a

WORD BANK

cat   hat   mat   pat   rat   sat   vat   fat

Find the missing words.

The cat saw a _____
on the _____ .

The fat _____ could
not catch the _____ .

Do not _____
the dog, he may bite.

Now write the other words.

_____   _____   _____

Name: _____ **Date:** _____

Words for today

cat _____ _____

mat _____ _____

pat _____ _____

rat _____ _____

sat _____ _____

fat _____ _____

  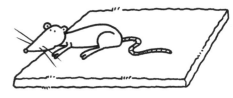

Learning objective	
Phonemes Consonants: /h/, /l/, /p/, /r/, /s/, /z/ Vowel: /i/	**Target words** hip, lip, pip, rip, sip, zip

Teacher's notes

Sheet 10a

- Photocopy this page and cut out the letter tiles.

- Revise the sounds with the child. Depending on your school's policy, you may decide to use the letter names as well as the sounds, saying, for example, 'This is letter **r** and it says /r/.' Pronounce the phoneme as it would sound when used in a word, without any additional sounds, e.g. the sound that **r** makes at the start of the word *rip* is quite short and subtle.

- When you feel the child is confident with some or all of the phonemes, arrange the letter tiles to make the words *hip, lip, pip, rip, sip, zip*. Help the child blend the phonemes to say the words.

Sheet 10b

- When you feel the child is ready, look at Sheet 10b together. Ask him/her to point to the letters at the top of the page and to tell you the sounds they make.

- Dictate the words **hip**, **lip**, **pip**, **rip**, **sip**, **zip** one at a time, helping the child segment each word into its phonemes so that s/he can choose the correct letters to match the words. Each word can then be stuck in position on the worksheet and the child can copy the words on to the writing lines underneath.

- As an additional activity you could make up some oral sentences together using some of the words and pointing to these words as you say them, e.g. *A pip fell out of my apple*. Write down one of the sentences for the child to copy. Encourage him/her to write clearly, following the school's handwriting policy, and to start the sentence with a capital letter and to finish with a full stop.

Sheet 10c

- This sheet includes six words with the medial vowel **i** and the final consonant **p**. It could be photocopied for display purposes but could also be used to provide extra practice in writing the words.

- There are three writing lines for each word, one for writing the target word quite large and the other two for smaller writing practice. You could write each word on the first of the two smaller writing lines so that the child can copy your writing in the correct style used by your school.

LETTER TILES

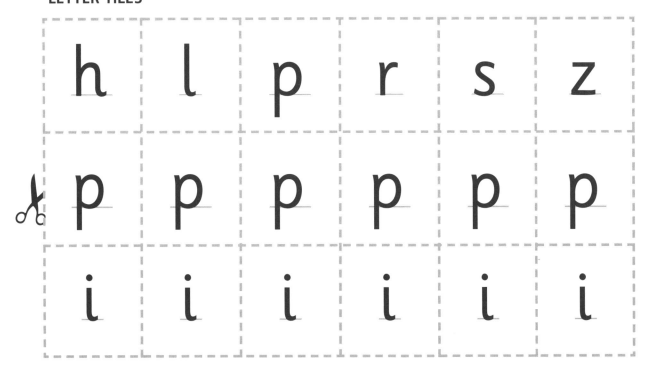

Name: _____   **Date:** _____

What sounds do the letters make?

h l p r s z i

Listen to your teacher.
Stick on letters to make the words.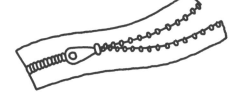

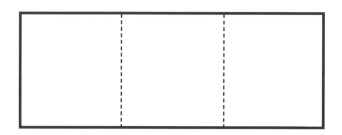

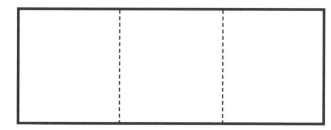

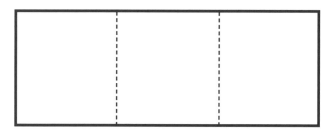

Andrew Brodie: Supporting Phonics & Spelling © A & C Black Publishers Ltd. 2006

Name: **Date:**

Words for today

hip

lip

pip

rip

sip

zip

11a

Phonemes
Consonants: /b/, /f/, /k/, /l/, /p/, /s/, /t/
Vowel: /i/

Target words
bit, fit, kit, lit, pit, sit

Teacher's notes

Sheet 11a

- Photocopy this page and cut out the letter tiles.

- Revise the sounds with the child. Depending on your school's policy, you may decide to use the letter names as well as the sounds, saying, for example, 'This is letter **t** and it says /t/.' Pronounce the phoneme as it would sound when used in a word, without any additional sounds.

- When you feel the child is confident with some or all of the phonemes, arrange the letter tiles to make the words *bit, fit, kit, lit, pit, sit*. Help the child blend the phonemes to say the words.

Sheet 11b

- When you feel the child is ready, look at Sheet 11b together. Ask him/her to point to the letters at the top of the page and to tell you the sounds they make.

- Dictate the words **bit, fit, kit, lit, pit, sit** one at a time, helping the child segment each word into its phonemes so that s/he can choose the correct letters to match the words.

- As an additional activity you could make up some oral sentences together using some of the words and pointing to these words as you say them, e.g. *Did the new football kit fit? Sit still for a bit*. Write down one of the sentences for the child to copy. Encourage him/her to write clearly, following the school's handwriting policy, and to start the sentence with a capital letter and to finish with a full stop.

Sheet 11c

- This sheet includes six words with the medial vowel **i** and the final consonant **t**. It could be photocopied for display purposes but could also be used to provide extra practice in writing the words.

- There are three writing lines for each word, one for writing the word quite large and the other two for smaller writing practice. You could write each word on the first of the two smaller writing lines so that the child can copy your writing in the correct style used by your school.

LETTER TILES

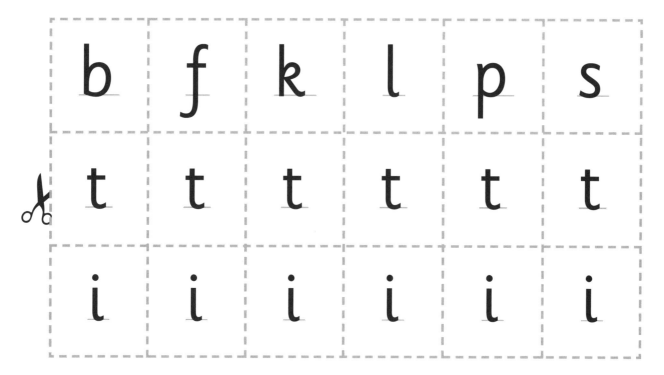

Name: _____   **Date:** _____

What sounds do the letters make?

b f k l p s t i

Listen to your teacher. Write the words.

_____   _____

_____   _____

_____   _____

   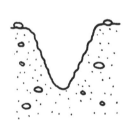      

Make up your own sentence using some of the words.

_____

_____

_____

Andrew Brodie: Supporting Phonics & Spelling © A & C Black Publishers Ltd. 2006

Name: **Date:**

Words for today

bit

fit

kit

lit

pit

sit

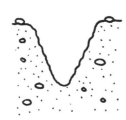

Andrew Brodie: Supporting Phonics & Spelling © A & C Black Publishers Ltd. 2006

Learning objective	
Phonemes **Consonants:** /b/, /f/, /d/, /h/, /m/, /n/, /p/, /t/ **Vowel:** /e/	**Target words** bed, fed, hen, men, pen, ten

12a

Teacher's notes

Sheet 12a

- Photocopy this page and cut out the letter tiles.
- Revise the sounds with the child. Depending on your school's policy, you may decide to use the letter names as well as the sounds, saying, for example, 'This is letter **h** and it says /h/.' Pronounce the phoneme as it would sound when used in a word, without any additional sounds. Encourage the child to say the word *hen* repeatedly listening to the sound made by the letter **h**.
- When you feel the child is confident with some or all of the phonemes, arrange the letter tiles to make the words *bed, fed, hen, men, pen, ten.* Help the child blend the phonemes to say the words.

Sheet 12b

- When you feel the child is ready, look at Sheet 12b together. Ask him/her to point to the letters at the top of the page and to tell you the sounds they make.
- Read the sentences with the missing words with the child and help him/her to write the words in the correct places.

Sheet 12c

- This sheet includes six words with the medial vowel **e** and the final consonants **d** or **n**. It could be photocopied for display purposes but could also be used to provide extra practice in writing the words.

- There are three writing lines for each word, one for writing the word quite large and the other two for smaller writing practice. You could write each word on the first of the two smaller writing lines so that the child can copy your writing in the correct style used by your school.

LETTER TILES

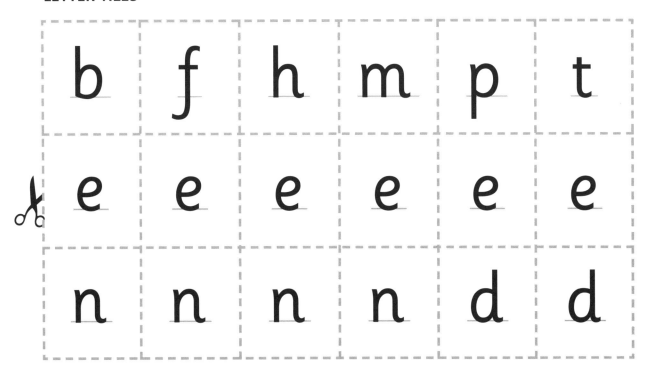

Name: **Date:**

What sounds do the letters make?

b f d h m n p t e

WORD BANK

bed fed led den hen men pen ten

Find the missing words.

Pam fell out of _____
when she was asleep.

Jan _____ the
_____ then closed
the chicken _____ .

Ten _____ came into
the field to play football.

Now write the other words.

_____   _____   _____

Andrew Brodie: Supporting Phonics & Spelling © A & C Black Publishers Ltd. 2006

Name: _____ **Date:** _____

Words for today

bed _____ _____

fed _____ _____

hen _____ _____

men _____ _____

pen _____ _____

ten _____ _____

Andrew Brodie: Supporting Phonics & Spelling © A & C Black Publishers Ltd. 2006

13a

Phonemes
Consonants: /b/, /g/, /l/, /p/, /r/, /w/
Vowels: /a/, /e/

Target words
bag, rag, wag, beg, leg, peg

Teacher's notes

Sheet 13a

- Photocopy this page and cut out the letter tiles.

- Revise the sounds with the child. Depending on your school's policy, you may decide to use the letter names as well as the sounds, saying, for example, 'This is letter **w** and it says /w/.' Pronounce the phoneme as it would sound when used in a word, without any additional sounds.

- When you feel the child is confident with some or all of the phonemes, arrange the letter tiles to make the words *bag, rag, wag, beg, leg, peg*. Help the child blend the phonemes to say the words.

Sheet 13b

- When you feel the child is ready, look at Sheet 13b together. Ask him/her to point to the letters at the top of the page and to tell you the sounds they make.

- Dictate the words **bag**, **rag**, **wag**, **beg**, **leg**, **peg** one at a time, helping the child segment each word into its phonemes so that s/he can choose the correct letters to match the words. Each word can then be stuck in position on the worksheet and the child can copy the words on to the writing lines underneath.

- As an additional activity you could make up some oral sentences together using some of the words and pointing to these words as you say them, e.g. *Did the dog wag its tail? Did the dog beg for a bone?* Write down one of the sentences for the child to copy. Encourage him/her to write clearly, following the school's handwriting policy, and to start the sentence with a capital letter and to finish with a full stop.

Sheet 13c

- This sheet includes six words with medial vowels **a** or **e** and the final consonant **g**. It could be photocopied for display purposes but could also be used to provide extra practice in writing the words.

- There are three writing lines for each word, one for writing the word quite large and the other two for smaller writing practice. You could write each word on the first of the two smaller writing lines so that the child can copy your writing in the correct style used by your school.

LETTER TILES

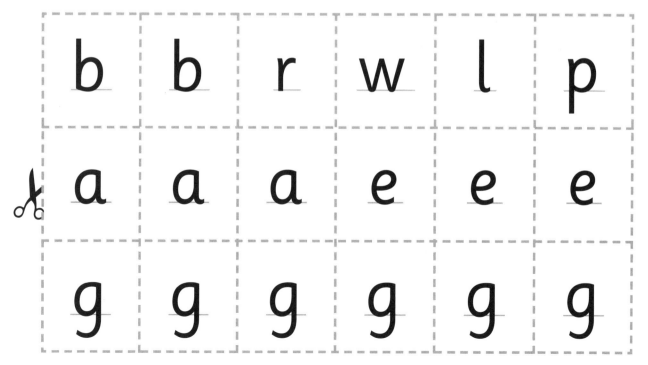

Name: **Date:**

What sounds do the letters make?

b g l p r w a e

Listen to your teacher.
Stick on letters to make the words.

Name: **Date:**

Words for today

bag

rag

wag

beg

leg

p e g

      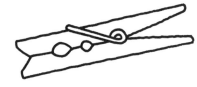

Learning objective	
Phonemes **Consonants:** /b/, /k/, /h/, /r/, /t/ **Vowels:** /i/, /u/	**Target words** cub, hub, rub, tub, bib, rib

Teacher's notes

Sheet 14a

- Photocopy this page and cut out the letter tiles.

- Revise the sounds with the child. Depending on your school's policy, you may decide to use the letter names as well as the sounds, saying, for example, 'This is letter **h** and it says /h/.' Pronounce the phoneme as it would sound when used in a word.

- When you feel the child is confident with some or all of the phonemes, arrange the letter tiles to make the words *cub, hub, rub, tub, bib, rib.* Help the child blend the phonemes to say the words.

Sheet 14b

- When you feel the child is ready, look at Sheet 14b together. Ask him/her to point to the letters at the top of the page and to tell you the sounds they make.

- Dictate the words **cub**, **hub**, **rub**, **tub**, **bib**, **rib** one at a time, helping the child segment each word into its phonemes so that s/he can choose the correct letters to match the words.

- As an additional activity you could make up some oral sentences together using some of the words and pointing to these words as you say them, e.g. *Have you seen a bear cub? The baby wore a bib.* Write down one of the sentences for the child to copy. Encourage him/her to write clearly, following the school's handwriting policy, and to start the sentence with a capital letter and to finish with a full stop.

Sheet 14c

- This sheet includes six words with the medial vowels **i** or **u** and the final consonant **b**. It could be photocopied for display purposes but could also be used to provide extra practice in writing the words.

- There are three writing lines for each word, one for writing the word quite large and the other two for smaller writing practice. You could write each word on the first of the two smaller writing lines so that the child can copy your writing in the correct style used by your school.

LETTER TILES

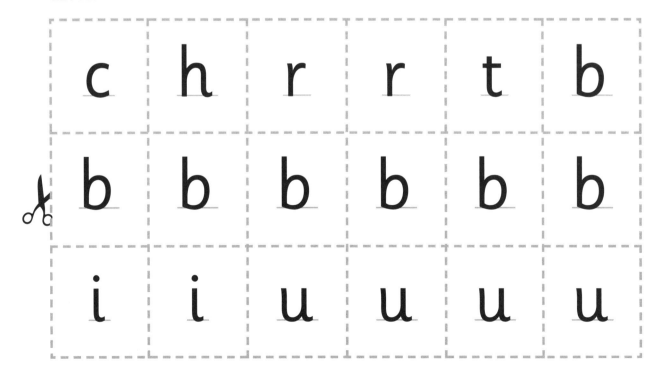

What sounds do the letters make?

b c h r t i u

Listen to your teacher. Write the words.

_____   _____

_____   _____

_____   _____

Make up your own sentence using some of the words.

_____

_____

_____

Andrew Brodie: Supporting Phonics & Spelling © A & C Black Publishers Ltd. 2006

Name: **Date:**

Words for today

c u b

h u b

r u b

t u b

b i b

r i b

Learning objective

| **Phonemes** Consonants: /d/, /g/, /h/, /j/, /m/, /r/ Vowel: /u/ | **Target words** dug, hug, jug, mug, rug, mum |

15a

Teacher's notes

Sheet 15a

- Photocopy this page and cut out the letter tiles.

- Revise the sounds with the child. Depending on your school's policy, you may decide to use the letter names as well as the sounds, saying, for example, 'This is letter **j** and it says /j/.' Pronounce the phoneme as it would sound when used in a word, without any additional sounds.

- When you feel the child is confident with some or all of the phonemes, arrange the letter tiles to make the words *dug, hug, jug, mug, rug, mum*. Help the child blend the phonemes to say the words.

Sheet 15b

- When you feel the child is ready, look at Sheet 15b together. Ask him/her to point to the letters at the top of the page and to tell you the sounds they make.

- Read the sentences with the missing words with the child and help him/her to write the words in the correct places.

Sheet 15c

- This sheet includes six words with the medial vowel **u** and the final consonant **g** or **m**. It could be photocopied for display purposes but could also be used to provide extra practice in writing the words.

- There are three writing lines for each word, one for writing the word quite large and the other two for smaller writing practice. You could write each word on the first of the two smaller writing lines so that the child can copy your writing in the correct style used by your school.

LETTER TILES

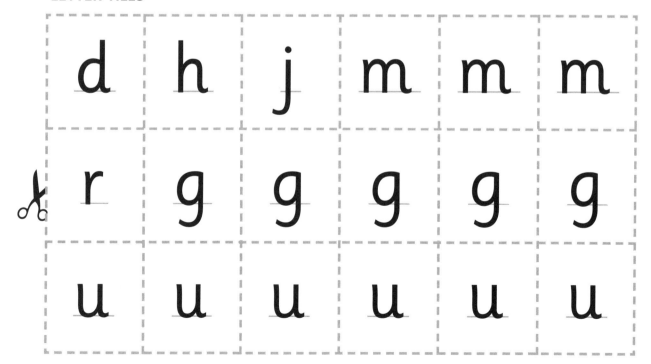

d h j m m m

r g g g g g

u u u u u u

Andrew Brodie: Supporting Phonics & Spelling © A & C Black Publishers Ltd. 2006

Name: **Date:**

What sounds do the letters make?

d   g   h   j   m   r   u

WORD BANK

bug   dug   hug   jug   mug   rug   mum

Find the missing words.

The _____

is full of water.

Mum is drinking tea

from a _____.

Mum _____ the

garden so that she could

plant some flowers.

Now write the other words.

_____   _____   _____

Andrew Brodie: Supporting Phonics & Spelling © A & C Black Publishers Ltd. 2006

Name: **Date:**

Words for today

dug

hug

jug

mug

rug

mum

Andrew Brodie: Supporting Phonics & Spelling © A & C Black Publishers Ltd. 2006

Learning objective	
Phonemes **Consonants:** /b/, /k/, /n/, /p/, /r/, /t/ **Vowel:** /u/	**Target words** but, nut, put, rut, cup, pup

Teacher's notes

Sheet 16a

- Photocopy this page and cut out the letter tiles.
- Revise the sounds with the child. Depending on your school's policy, you may decide to use the letter names as well as the sounds, saying, for example, 'This is letter **n** and it says /n/.' Pronounce the phoneme as it would sound when used in a word, without any additional sounds.
- When you feel the child is confident with some or all of the phonemes, arrange the letter tiles to make the words *but, nut, put, rut, cup, pup*. Help the child blend the phonemes to say the words.

Sheet 16b

- When you feel the child is ready, look at Sheet 16b together. Ask him/her to point to the letters at the top of the page and to tell you the sounds they make.
- Dictate the words **but**, **nut**, **put**, **rut**, **cup**, **pup** one at a time, helping the child segment each word into its phonemes so that s/he can choose the correct letters to match the words. Each word can then be stuck in position on the worksheet and the child can copy the words on to the writing lines underneath.
- As an additional activity you could make up some oral sentences together using some of the words and pointing to these words as you say them, e.g. *Put the nut in the cup. The wheel made a rut in the mud*. The second of these two example sentences is phonetically quite complicated. For example, the word *wheel* includes the phoneme /w/ or /wh/ (regional variation), the phoneme /ee/ and the phoneme /l/. We recommend that you encourage the children to focus on the target word *rut* and perhaps make comparison to the word *mud*.
- Write down one of the sentences for the child to copy. Encourage him/her to write clearly, following the school's handwriting policy, and to start the sentence with a capital letter and to finish with a full stop.

Sheet 16c

- This sheet includes six words with the medial vowel **u** and the final consonant **p** or **t**. It could be photocopied for display purposes but could also be used to provide extra practice in writing the words. There are three writing lines for each word, one for writing the word quite large and the other two for smaller writing practice. You could write each word on the first of the two smaller writing lines so that the child can copy your writing in the correct style used by your school.

LETTER TILES

b	n	p	p	p	p
r	c	t	t	t	t
u	u	u	u	u	u

Name: **Date:**

What sounds do the letters make?

b   c   n   p   r   t   u

Listen to your teacher.
Stick on letters to make the words.

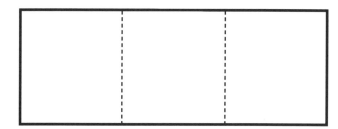

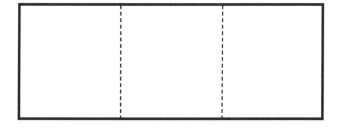

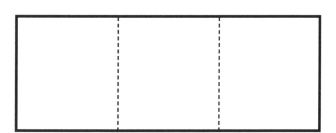

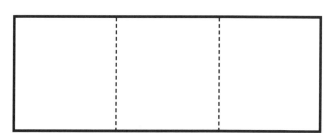

Andrew Brodie: Supporting Phonics & Spelling © A & C Black Publishers Ltd. 2006

Name: _____

Date: _____

Words for today

but _____ _____

nut _____ _____

put _____ _____

rut _____ _____

cup _____ _____

pup _____ _____

17a

Learning objective	Target words
Phonemes **Consonants:** /b/, /f/, /s/, /w/, /k/ **Vowels:** /a/, /i/, /o/	fax, fix, fox, wax, six, box

Teacher's notes

Sheet 17a

- Photocopy this page and cut out the letter tiles.
- Revise the sounds with the child. Depending on your school's policy, you may decide to use the letter names as well as the sounds, saying, for example, 'This is letter **x** and it says /k//s/.' Pronounce the phoneme as it would sound when used in a word, without any additional sounds.
- When you feel the child is confident with some or all of the phonemes, arrange the letter tiles to make the words *fax, fix, fox, wax, six, box*. Help the child blend the phonemes to say the words.

Sheet 17b

- When you feel the child is ready, look at Sheet 17b together. Ask him/her to point to the letters at the top of the page and to tell you the sounds they make.
- Dictate the words **fax, fix, fox, wax, six, box** one at a time, helping the child segment each word into its phonemes so that s/he can choose the correct letters to match the words. The words provide lots of opportunities for discussion. Help the child to hear the sounds that the letters make. Encourage them to notice that each word ends with the blend **ax, ix** or **ox**. Practising will help them to distinguish between the vowel phonemes /a/, /i/ and /o/.
- As an additional activity you could make up some oral sentences together using some of the words and pointing to these words as you say them, e.g. *The candle is made of wax. The fox chased six hens.* Write down one of the sentences for the child to copy. Encourage him/her to write clearly, following the school's handwriting policy, and to start the sentence with a capital letter and to finish with a full stop.

Sheet 17c

- This sheet includes six words with the medial vowels **i** or **o** and the final consonant **x**. It could be photocopied for display purposes but could also be used to provide extra practice in writing the words.
- There are three writing lines for each word, one for writing the word quite large and the other two for smaller writing practice. You could write each word on the first of the two smaller writing lines so that the child can copy your writing in the correct style used by your school.

LETTER TILES

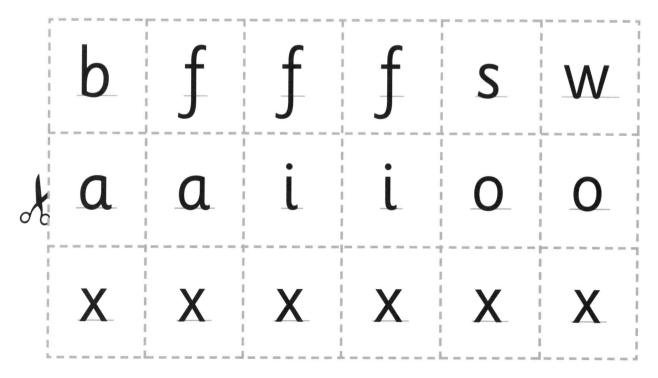

56

Andrew Brodie: Supporting Phonics & Spelling © A & C Black Publishers Ltd. 2006

Name: **Date:**

What sounds do the letters make?

b f s w x a i o

Listen to your teacher. Write the words.

_____   _____

_____   _____

_____   _____

Make up your own sentence using some of the words.

_____

_____

_____

Andrew Brodie: Supporting Phonics & Spelling © A & C Black Publishers Ltd. 2006

Name: **Date:**

Words for today

fax

fix

fox

wax

six

box

    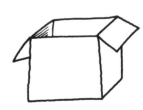

Andrew Brodie: Supporting Phonics & Spelling © A & C Black Publishers Ltd. 2006

Learning objective

Phonemes **Consonants:** /b/, /d/, /f/, /g/, /m/, /n/, /s/ **Vowel:** /u/	**Target words** bud, mud, bun, fun, sun, bus

Teacher's notes

Sheet 18a

- Photocopy this page and cut out the letter tiles.

- Revise the sounds with the child. Depending on your school's policy, you may decide to use the letter names as well as the sounds, saying, for example, 'This is letter **s** and it says /s/.' Pronounce the phoneme as it would sound when used in a word, without any additional sounds.

- When you feel the child is confident with some or all of the phonemes, arrange the letter tiles to make the words *bud, mud, bun, fun, sun, bus.* Help the child blend the phonemes to say the words.

Sheet 18b

- When you feel the child is ready, look at Sheet 18b together. Ask him/her to point to the letters at the top of the page and to tell you the sounds they make.

- Read the sentences with the missing words with the child and support him/her in writing the words in the correct places. The words provide lots of opportunities for discussion. Help the children to hear the sounds that the letters make. Encourage them to notice that most of the words end with the blends **ud** or **un**. Can they spot the odd one out? Looking at the words *bud*, *bun* and *bus* gives an opportunity to compare the phonemes /d/, /n/ and /s/.

Sheet 18c

- This sheet includes six words with the medial vowel **u** and the final consonant **d**, **n** or **s**. It could be photocopied for display purposes but could also be used to provide extra practice in writing the words.

- There are three writing lines for each word, one for writing the word quite large and the other two for smaller writing practice. You could write each word on the first of the two smaller writing lines so that the child can copy your writing in the correct style used by your school.

LETTER TILES

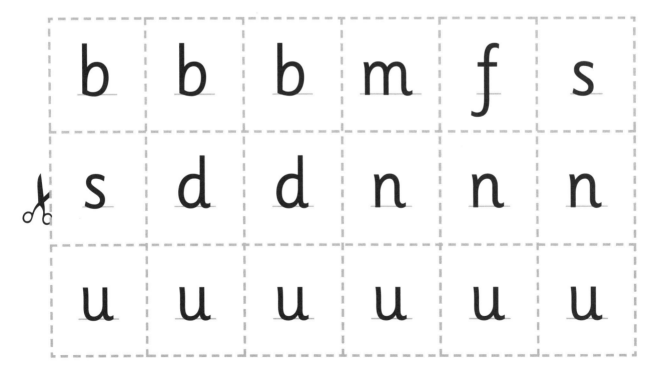

b	b	b	m	f	s
s	s	d	d	n	n	n
u	u	u	u	u	u

What sounds do the letters make?

b d f g m n s u

WORD BANK

bud mud sud bun gun fun sun bus

Find the missing words.

Playing in the _____
is lots of _____.

The baby began to cry
when a soap _____
went in her eye.

I went to the shops
on a _____.

Now write the other words.

_____ _____ _____ _____

Name: **Date:**

Words for today

bud

mud

bun

fun

sun

bus

19a

Learning objective

Phonemes
Consonants: /b/, /k/, /m/, /n/, /p/, /s/, /t/, /v/, /w/
Vowels: /a/, /e/, /i/, /o/, /u/

Target words
van, web, six, mop, bus, cat

Teacher's notes

Sheet 19a

- Photocopy this page and cut out the letter tiles.

- Revise the sounds with the child. Depending on your school's policy, you may decide to use the letter names as well as the sounds, saying, for example, 'This is letter **v** and it says /v/.' Try saying the word *van* repeatedly, then just saying the phenome /v/ at the start of the word.

- Play matching games with another photocopied set of the same letters or magnetic letters.

Sheet 19b

- When you feel the child is ready, look at Sheet 19b together. Ask him/her to point to the letters at the top of the page and to tell you the sounds they make.

- Dictate the words **van**, **web**, **six**, **mop**, **bus**, **cat** one at a time, helping the child segment each word into its phonemes so that s/he can choose the correct letters to match the words. Each word can then be stuck in position on the worksheet and the child can copy the words on to the writing lines underneath.

- As an additional activity you could make up some oral sentences together using some of the words and pointing to these words as you say them, e.g. *There were six spiders in the web. I saw a van and a bus.* Write down one of the sentences for the child to copy. Encourage him/her to write clearly, following the school's handwriting policy, and to start the sentence with a capital letter and to finish with a full stop.

Sheet 19c

- This sheet includes six words with the medial vowel sounds /a/, /e/, /i/, /o/ or /u/. Ask the child which two words have the same vowel sound in the middle. It could be photocopied for display purposes but could also be used to provide extra practice in writing the words.

- There are three writing lines for each word, one for writing the word quite large and the other two for smaller writing practice. You could write each word on the first of the two smaller writing lines so that the child can copy your writing in the correct style used by your school.

LETTER TILES

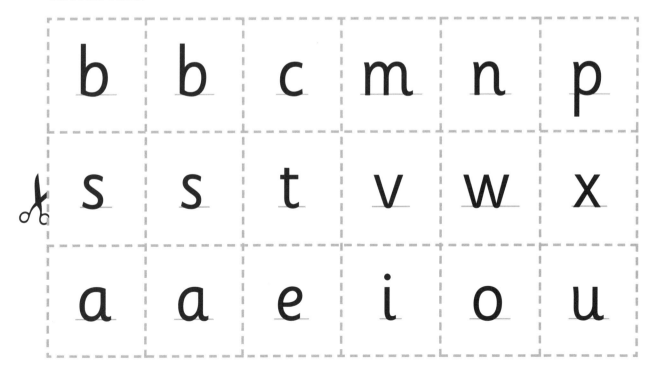

Name: **Date:**

What sounds do the letters make?

b c m n p s t v
w x a e i o u

Listen to your teacher.
Stick on letters to make the words.

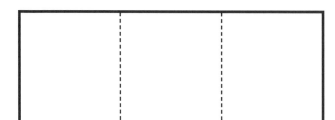

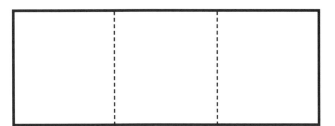

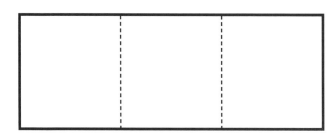

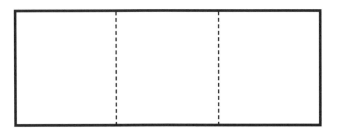

Name: **Date:**

Words for today

van

web

six

mop

bus

cat

Andrew Brodie: Supporting Phonics & Spelling © A & C Black Publishers Ltd. 2006